PEANUT BUTTER AND JELLY

BEN CLANTON

tundra

FOR ALEX COX!
KEEP SPREADING THE AWESOMENESS!

Text and illustrations copyright © 2018 by Ben Clanton
This paperback edition published by Tundra Books, 2019

Tundra Books, an imprint of Penguin Random House Canada Young Readers, a Penguin Random House Company

Library and Archives Canada Cataloguing in Publication

Clanton, Ben, 1988-, author, illustrator
Peanut butter and Jelly / Ben Clanton.

(A Narwhal and Jelly book)
Issued in print and electronic formats.
ISBN 978-0-7352-6245-4 (hardcover).–ISBN 978-0-7352-6246-1 (softcover)
ISBN 978-0-7352-6247-8 (epub)

I. Title. II. Series: Clanton, Ben, 1988- . Narwhal and Jelly book

PZ7.C523Pea 2019   j813'.6   C2018-901240-4

Published simultaneously in the United States of America by Tundra Books of Northern New York,
an imprint of Penguin Random House Canada Young Readers, a Penguin Random House Company

Library of Congress Control Number: 2017939300

Edited by Tara Walker and Jessica Burgess
Designed by Ben Clanton and Andrew Roberts
The artwork in this book was rendered in colored pencil, watercolor and ink, and colored digitally.
The text was handlettered by Ben Clanton.

Photos: (waffle) © Tiger Images/Shutterstock; (strawberry) © Valentina Razumova/Shutterstock;
(pickle) © dominitsky/Shutterstock; (boom box) © valio84sl/Thinkstock; (jars) © choness/Thinkstock;
(peanuts) © Zoonar/homydesign/Thinkstock; (jam on bread) © George Doyle/Thinkstock;
(peanut butter toast) © NicholasBPhotography/Thinkstock

Printed and bound in China

www.penguinrandomhouse.ca

1 2 3 4 5   23 22 21 20 19

CONTENTS

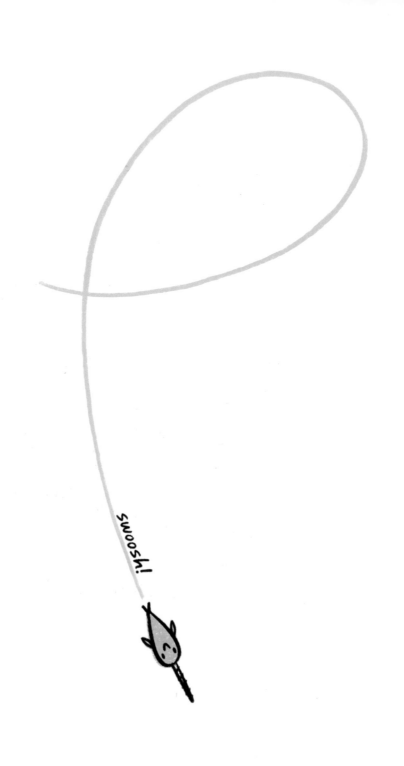

swoosh!

A SWEET AND SALTY STORY!

AHOY, JELLY!
WHAT IS THAT SMALL, STRANGE WAFFLE YOU'RE EATING?

nom
nom
nom

UM...NARWHAL,
THIS IS **NOT** A WAFFLE.
IT IS A PEANUT BUTTER
COOKIE.

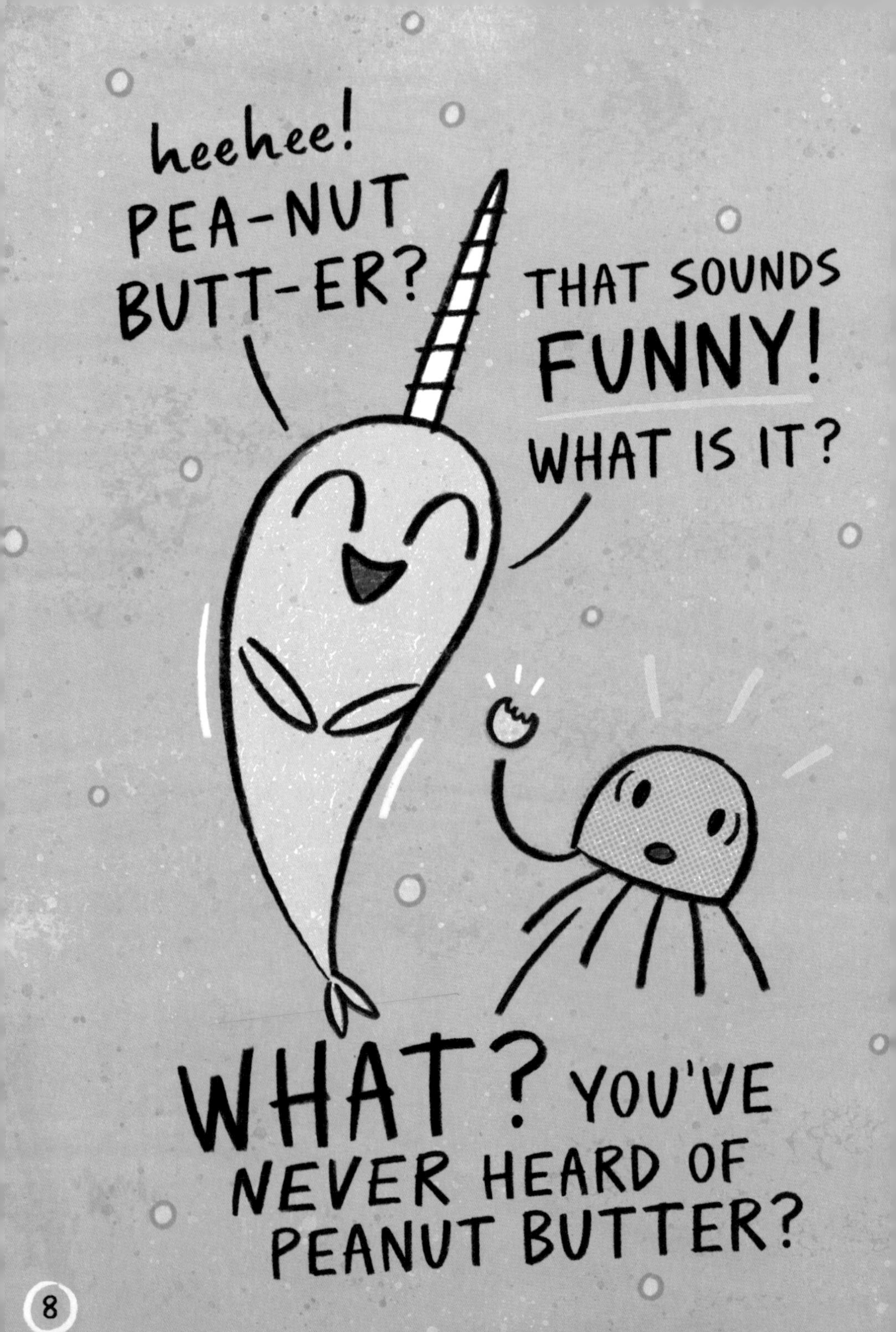
heehee!
PEA-NUT BUTT-ER?
THAT SOUNDS FUNNY!
WHAT IS IT?
WHAT? YOU'VE NEVER HEARD OF PEANUT BUTTER?

YUCK!

HAVE YOU ACTUALLY EATEN SOMETHING LIKE THAT BEFORE?

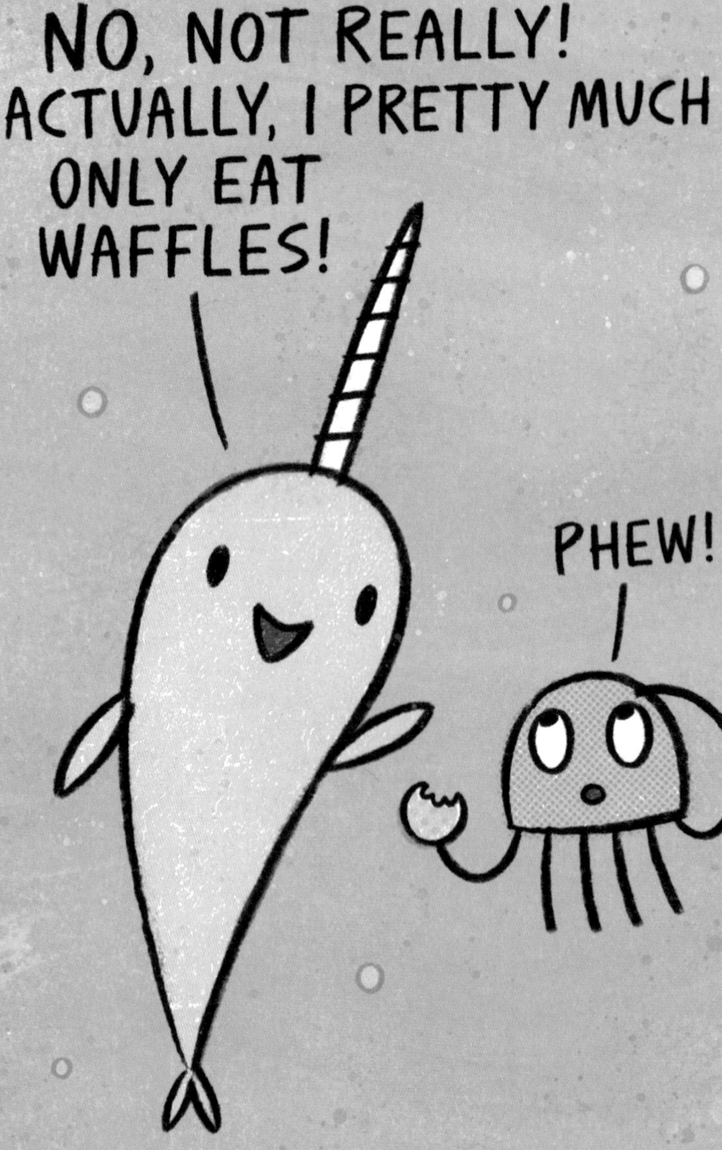
NO, NOT REALLY! ACTUALLY, I PRETTY MUCH ONLY EAT WAFFLES!
PHEW!

WAIT A MINUTE...
ONLY WAFFLES?

CAKE? APPLES?
CHEESE? PIE?
ARTICHOKES?
    MARSHMALLOWS?
GUACAMOLE?
    UH...SUSHI?
FRENCH FRIES?

19

WHY?

HAVE YOU EVER HEARD OF "TOO MUCH OF A GOOD THING"?

THAT'S SILLY! HOW CAN YOU HAVE TOO MANY WAFFLES?

RIGHT... NEVER MIND.

BUT MAYBE YOU'LL LIKE THIS COOKIE EVEN MORE THAN WAFFLES!

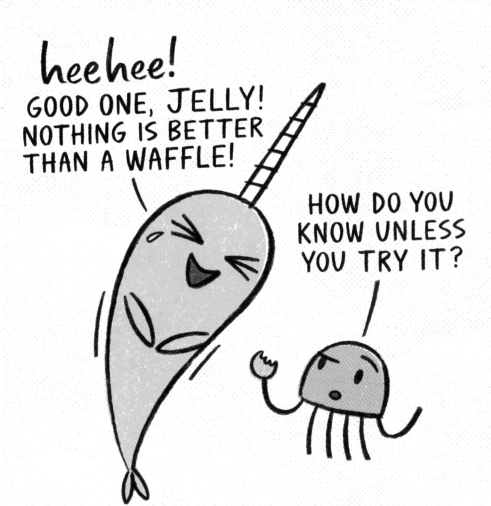

I TELL YOU WHAT,
I'LL MAKE YOU AN
EXTRA LARGE
WAFFLE IF YOU JUST
TRY THIS PEANUT
BUTTER COOKIE.

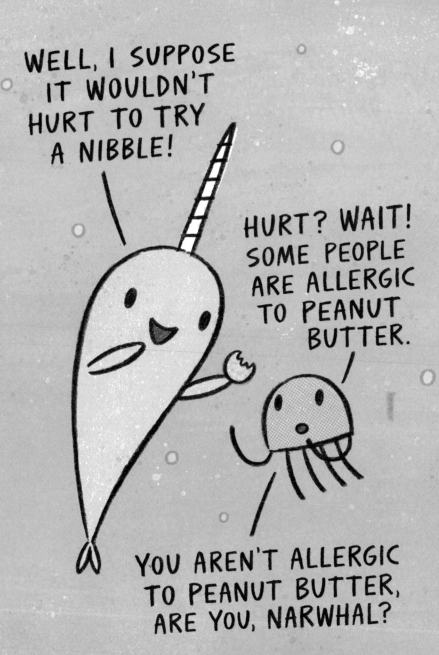

ALLERGIC?

DON'T THINK SO!*

BUT I ONCE KNEW A SEA HORSE WHO COULDN'T EAT WAFFLES...IT WAS THE SADDEST THING I'VE EVER HEARD. YET SHE SWORE SHE WAS HAPPY SO LONG AS SHE COULD EAT GUMMY BEARS.

*THE ALLERGIC AQUATIC ANIMALS AWARENESS ASSOCIATION ADVISES CAUTION WHEN TRYING A COMMON ALLERGEN.

IT'S FINTASTIC!

DELICIOUS FACTS

SCIENTISTS BELIEVE NARWHALS SUCK UP THEIR FOOD WHOLE AND EAT MAINLY FISH.

I PREFER WAFFLES!

AND PEANUT BUTTER!

MOST JELLYFISH STING THEIR PREY WITH THEIR TENTACLES BEFORE EATING IT.

BLUE WHALES (THE LARGEST ANIMAL EVER) EAT MAINLY TINY LITTLE KRILL. THEY EAT OODLES OF THEM. AS MANY AS 40 MILLION KRILL PER DAY!

YUM!

EEK!

HUMPBACK WHALES WORK TOGETHER TO CREATE COMPLEX BUBBLE NETS TO CORRAL FISH TO EAT.

SEA CUCUMBERS EAT ALL SORTS OF THINGS, INCLUDING POOP.

TIGER SHARKS ARE OFTEN REFERRED TO AS "THE TRASH CANS OF THE SEA" BECAUSE THEY WILL EAT JUST ABOUT ANYTHING, FROM PIGS TO TIRES TO EXPLOSIVES.

WHAT? YOU CAN'T JUST CHANGE YOUR NAME!

WHY NOT?

BECAUSE! IT ISN'T NORMAL!

OH.

WELL, I'VE NEVER REALLY WANTED TO BE NORMAL. BESIDES, THIS ISN'T THE FIRST TIME I'VE CHANGED MY NAME.

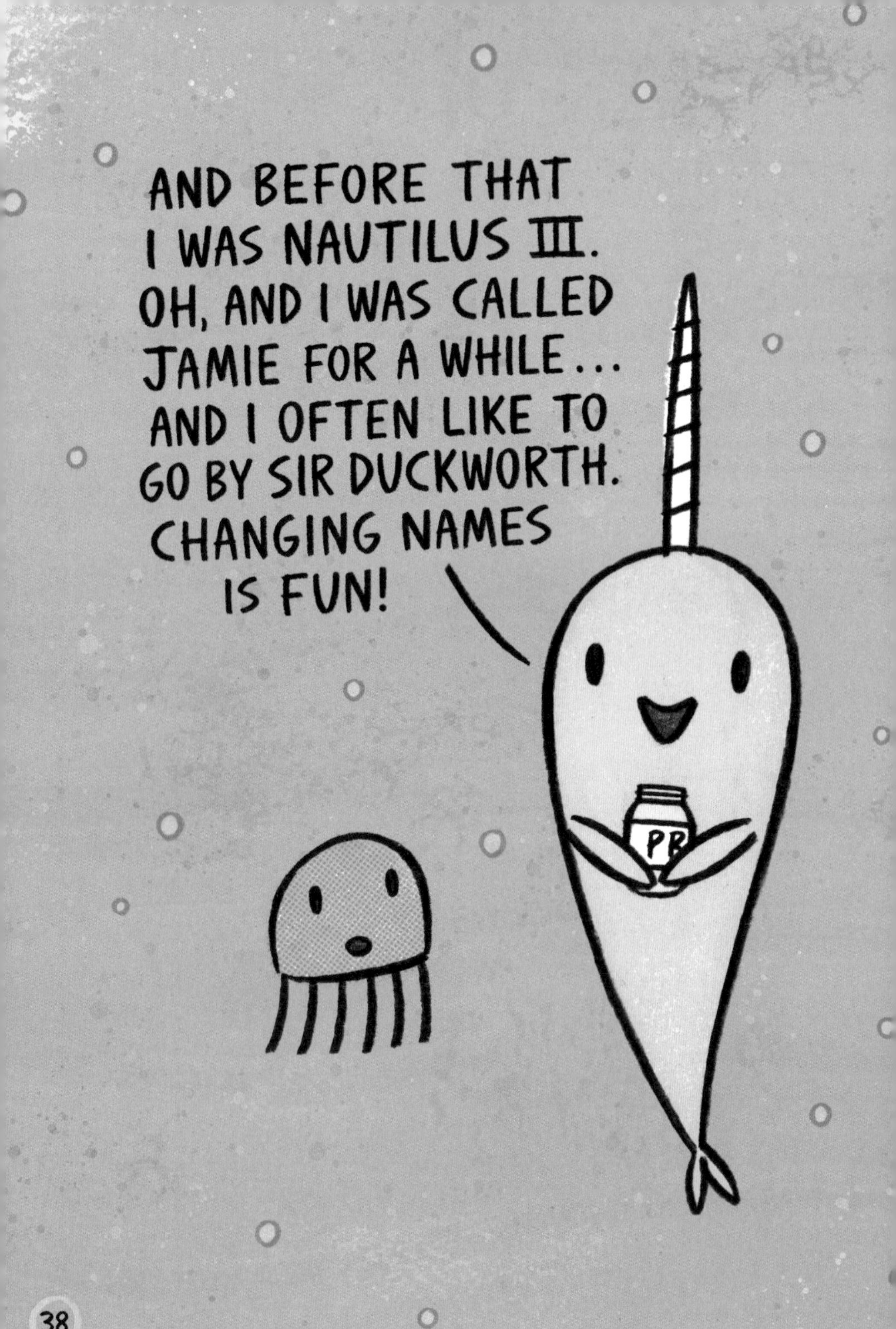
AND BEFORE THAT I WAS NAUTILUS III. OH, AND I WAS CALLED JAMIE FOR A WHILE... AND I OFTEN LIKE TO GO BY SIR DUCKWORTH. CHANGING NAMES IS FUN!
PB

UGH! LOOK, PEANUT BUTTER OR NARWHAL OR FRED OR WHATEVER YOU ARE CALLING YOURSELF... DON'T YOU THINK YOU'RE TAKING THIS PEANUT BUTTER THING A BIT TOO FAR?

FLOYD...

SUPER WAFFLE
AND STRAWBERRY SIDEKICK
VS. PB&J

by ~~Narwhal~~ Peanut Butter and ~~Jelly~~ Floyd

SUPER WAFFLE AND STRAWBERRY SIDEKICK HAVE BEATEN ANGRY ROBOTS AND VILLAINOUS BLOBS, SO THIS PICKLE WILL BE A PIECE OF CAKE ... PIECE OF PICKLE?

PEANUT

A.K.A. mini
NARWHAL

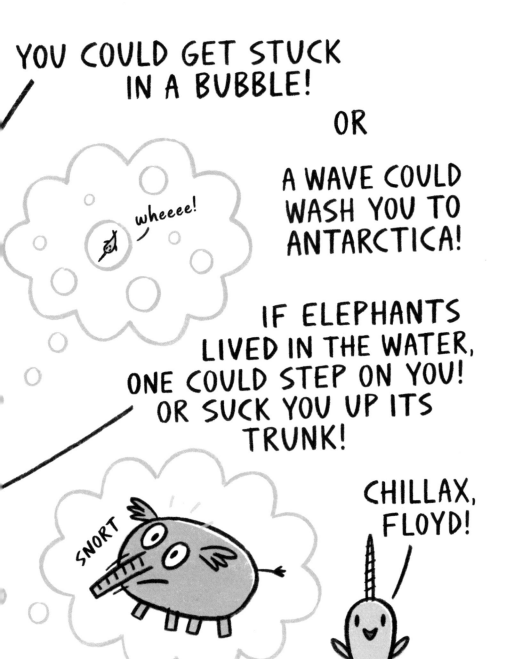

 NOW THAT I AM SUPER SMALL ALL THE WAFFLES WILL SEEM **HUGE** TO ME!

 I CAN EAT **GIANT** WAFFLES!

 OH.

 GOOD POINT!

THE NEXT DAY...

...NOW THAT I'M **ENORMOUS** I CAN EAT OODLES OF WAFFLES! I'LL BREAK THE **WORLD** RECORD FOR WAFFLE EATING!

THAT IS... INGENIOUS!

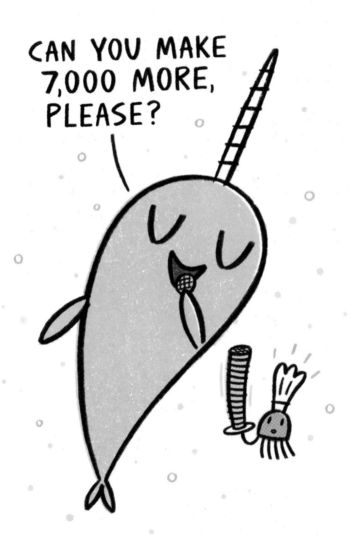